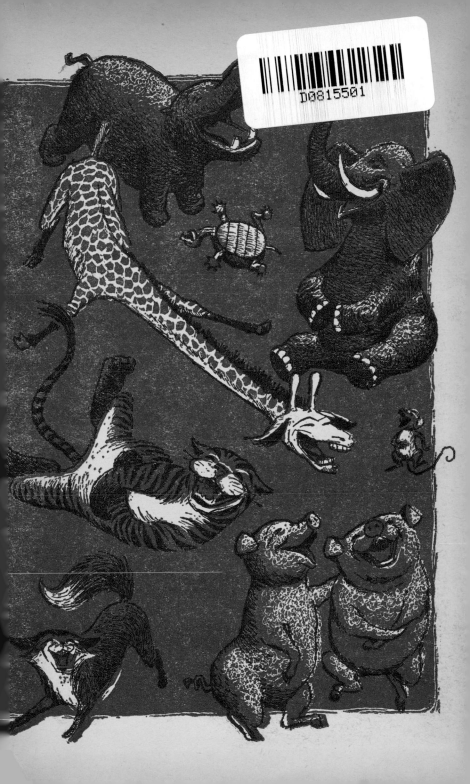

WHY THIS IS AN EASY READER

- This book has been carefully written to keep the young reader's interest high.

- It is written in a simple, open style, with a strong rhythm that adds enjoyment both to reading aloud and silent reading.

- There is a very high percentage of words repeated. It is this skillful repetition which helps the child to read independently. Seeing words again and again, he "practices" the vocabulary he knows, and learns with ease the words that are new.

- Only 284 different words have been used, with plurals and root words counted once.

  Almost one-half of the total vocabulary in this story has been used at least three times.
  Almost one-fifth of the total vocabulary has been used at least six times.
  Some words have been used 15, 22 and 44 times.

ABOUT THIS BOOK

- There is no more foolproof way to find out what fun a book can be than to read and chuckle at a printed page.

- Here are jokes and riddles to hear or read—then to reread and to try out on others. It is especially recommended as book-bait for the youngster who is still book-shy.

Jokes and Riddles

Written by JONATHAN PETER
Pictures by DAVID LOCKHART
Editorial Consultant: LILIAN MOORE

WONDER BOOKS
A Division of Grosset & Dunlap, Inc.
New York, N. Y. 10010

Introduction

These books are meant to help the young reader discover what a delightful experience reading can be. The stories are such fun that they urge the child to try his new reading skills. They are so easy to read that they will encourage and strengthen him as a reader.

The adult will notice that the sentences aren't too long, the words aren't too hard, and the skillful repetition is like a helping hand. What the child will feel is: "This is a good story—and I can read it myself!"

For some children, the best way to meet these stories may be to hear them read aloud at first. Others, who are better prepared to read on their own, may need a little help in the beginning—help that is best given freely. Youngsters who have more experience in reading alone—whether in first or second or third grade—will have the immediate joy of reading "all by myself."

These books have been planned to help all young readers grow—in their pleasure in books and in their power to read them.

Lilian Moore
Specialist in Reading
Formerly of Division of Instructional Research,
New York City Board of Education

Why is a barn

so noisy?

I give up.

Because the cows have horns.

Johnny ran into the house.

"Hi, Mom!" he called.

"What are we having for supper?
I hope we have lots of things."

"We do,"
said his mother.
"Lots and lots and lots
of things."

"Good," said Johnny.

"What are they?"

"Beans!" said his mother.

Father was trying to shave.

"Oooh!" he said.

"ow! ow!"

"What is the matter?"
Mother called.

"This brush is no good,"
said Father.
"I can't shave with it."

"That's funny," said Tommy.

"It was good this morning.

I know. I washed my bike with it."

14

What kind of beans

will not grow in a garden?

I give up.

Jelly beans!

All the boys and girls in the
class were making pictures.

Miss Hill said, "Now I will look
at your pictures."

She looked at Jenny's picture.

It was a picture of a house.

She looked at Peter's picture.

It was a picture of a dog.

18

She looked at Mike's picture.

"What is this?" she asked.

"It is a picture of a cow
in the grass," said Mike.

"Where is the grass?"
asked Miss Hill.

"Oh," said Mike, "the cow
ate up all the grass."

"And where is the cow?"
asked Miss Hill.

"The cow went to look for
more grass to eat," said Mike.

Why did the boy cut a hole
in his umbrella?

 I give up.

So he could see when
it stopped raining!

A big table was stuck in
the little doorway.

Ben and Bill worked and worked
to move the table.

But the table did not move.

"My, it is hard to push
this table in!" said Bill.

"In?" said Ben.
"I am trying to push it OUT!"

"Guess what I just saw,"
Lenny said to Kenny.
"I saw ten lions!"

"No!" said Kenny.

"Yes," said Lenny.
"And I saw ten tigers
and ten elephants, too!
They were all around me."

"What did you DO?"
Kenny asked.

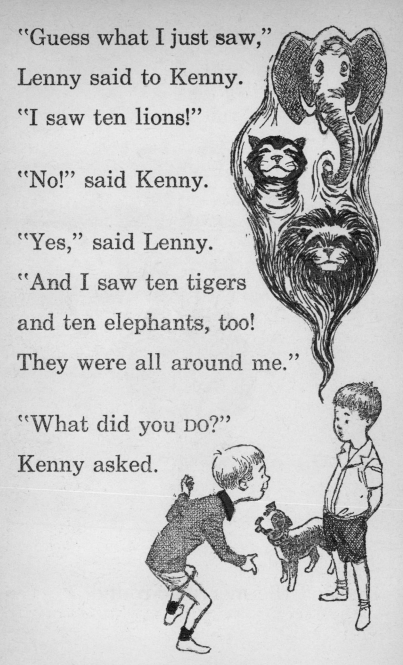

"I got off the merry-go-round!"
Lenny said.

What is the best thing to put
into an ice-cream soda?

 I give up.

A straw!

Farmer Brown walked into

Farmer Gray's barn.

Drip. Drip.

Water was coming down

from the roof.

"Why don't you fix that roof?"
asked Farmer Brown.

"It is raining,"
said Farmer Gray.
"I don't want to get wet."

The next day the sun came out.

Farmer Brown went to see
his friend again.

"Why don't you fix that roof
today?" he asked.

"I don't have to,"
said Farmer Gray.
"No water is coming down
into the barn today."

Why do you go to bed at night?

I give up.

Because the bed will not come
to you!

"Benny," said Jenny,
"what are you doing?"

"I am looking in the mirror,"
said Benny.

"But how can you see?

Your eyes are closed," said Jenny.

"I want to see how I look

when I am sleeping," said Benny.

Jerry had a cold.

The doctor came to see him.

"Let me look in your ears,"
said the doctor.

Jerry let him look.

"Now open your mouth,"
said the doctor.

Jerry opened his mouth.

"Now stick out your tongue,"
said the doctor.

"Why?" asked Jerry.
"I am not mad at you!"

What is the best way

to raise strawberries?

 I give up.

With a spoon!

It was a hot day.

Some people were sitting

on the steps of the house.

A man came by.

The man said to Sam,

"Does Mr. Bungle live

in this house?"

"Yes," said Sam.

"Can you show me where he lives?"
the man asked.

"This way," said Sam.

They walked up
and up
and up.
They walked all the way up
to the top of the house.

"He lives here," said Sam.

The man rang the bell.

He rang
and rang
and rang.

"He is not home,"
said the man.
"Do you know where he is?"

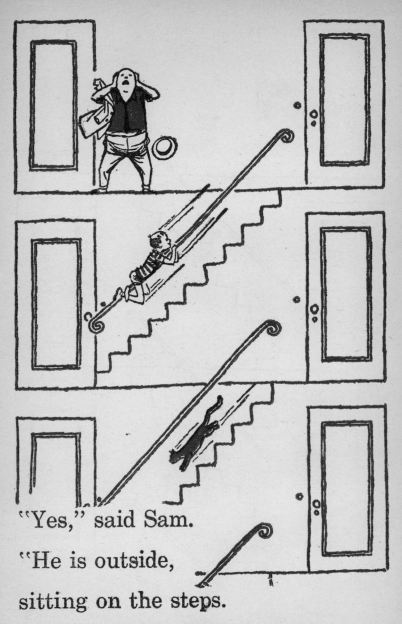

"Yes," said Sam.

"He is outside,
sitting on the steps.
You passed him as you came in."

What is a thing
with a wing
with a sting?

PING

I give up.

A bee.

Billy ran into the house.

"Billy," said his mother,
"what were you doing?"

"I was just playing
with my friends," said Billy.

"But look at your pants!
Look at your shirt!"
said his mother.

"Oh," said Billy,

"we were playing store.

I was the Swiss cheese!"

Joey called for Janie.

But Janie did not look happy.

"What's the matter?"
Joey asked.

"My tooth is loose,"
she told him.
"What can I do?"

"Run to the store
and get some paste,"
Joey said.

Janie ran down the street.

Then she stopped.

"What kind of paste shall I get?"
she called.

"Toothpaste, of course,"
said Joey.

When will a big black bear
come into a house?

I give up.

When the door is open.

Mother looked out the window.

She saw little Tommy crying.
She saw his brother Marty
on the sled.
He was going down the hill.

"What's the matter, Tommy?"
his mother called.

"Marty has the sled all the time,"
Tommy said.

"Marty!" his mother called.
"You must let your little brother
have the sled some of the time,
too."

"But I do," said Marty.
"I have it going down the hill.
And he has it going up!"

"I am going to make a
strawberry pie for supper,"
said Mother.

"May I help?"
asked Sally.

"Yes," said her mother.
"You may wash the strawberries."

Sally's mother gave her
a pan of strawberries.

Soon Sally's mother called,
"Are you washing all the
strawberries?
Are you doing a good job?"

"Oh, yes, Mother,"
said Sally.
"I am using lots of soap!"

How can you go out of the room
with two legs and come back
with six?

 I give up.

Bring a chair back with you.

One morning Bobby came
to school late.

"Bobby," the teacher said,
"you were late for school
yesterday.
You were late the day before.
And you are late again today.
What is the matter?"

"I can't help it,"
said Bobby.
"I run down Main Street
every day.
Then I come to a sign.
The sign says:

SCHOOL—GO SLOW.

So I do!"

CHOOSE FROM THESE EASY READERS